Elrose Hunter and Eir

Paul
THE FEARLESS ADVENTURER

Copyright © Elrose Hunter 2004
First published 2004
Reprinted 2008

ISBN 978 1 84427 078 1

Scripture Union, 207–209 Queensway, Bletchley, Milton Keynes, MK2 2EB, England
Email:info@scriptureunion.org.uk
Website:www.scriptureunion.org.uk

Scripture Union Australia
Locked Bag 2, Central Coast Business Centre, NSW 2252, Australia
Website:www.scriptureunion.org.au

Scripture Union USA
PO Box 987, Valley Forge, PA 19482, USA
Website:www.scriptureunion.org

The right of Elrose Hunter to be identified as author of this work has been asserted by her in accordance with the Copyright, Designs and Patents Act 1988.

The right of Eira Reeves to be identified as illustrator of this work has been asserted by her in accordance with the Copyright, Designs and Patents Act 1988.

Scripture quotations are from the Contemporary English Version published by Harper Collins Publishers, copyright © 1991, 1992, 1995 American Bible Society.

British Library Cataloguing-in-Publication Data.
A catalogue record of this book is available from the British Library.

Printed and bound in Singapore by Tien Wah Press Ltd.

Cover design:fourninezerodesign

Scripture Union is an international Christian charity working with churches in more than 130 countries, providing resources to bring the good news about Jesus Christ to children, young people and families and to encourage them to develop spiritually through the Bible and prayer.

As well as our network of volunteers, staff and associates who run holidays, church-based events and school Christian groups, we produce a wide range of publications and support those who use our resources through training programmes.

Paul lived hundreds of years ago when the Romans ruled the world. He lived in Jerusalem for a time and learned about the Jewish faith from a teacher called a rabbi.

Use the code to find the missing words in this verse, which every Jewish child learned by heart.

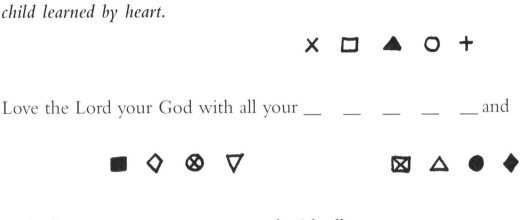

Love the Lord your God with all your __ __ __ __ __ and

with all your __ __ __ __ and with all your __ __ __ __.

A = ▲
D = ◆
E = □
H = ✕
I = △
L = ▽
M = ⊠
N = ●
O = ◇
R = ○
S = ■
T = ✝
U = ⊗

Paul did not always love Jesus. He thought that the followers of Jesus were not doing what God wanted, so he was cruel to them. One day he was riding along a road on his way to attack more believers. A very bright light startled his horse and Paul fell off and lay on the ground. God was stopping Paul from doing more harm.

Colour in the picture.

Jesus spoke to Paul as he lay on the ground. "I am Jesus. I am the one you are so cruel to. Get up and go into the city. You will be told what to do." Paul opened his eyes but he couldn't see anything! He had to be led into the city where he waited for three days to hear what God wanted him to do.

Guide Paul through the maze to the city and join the dots to spell the name of the city.

For three days Paul was blind and had nothing to eat or drink. Then a man called Ananias came to visit him. He said to Paul, "Jesus has sent me. He wants you to be able to see and to be filled with the Holy Spirit." It was the most wonderful thing that had ever happened to Paul.

Put the words in the right order to find out what happened next to Paul.

_____ _____ _____ _____ _____ _____.

Paul was completely changed by his meeting with Jesus. Now he told everybody that Jesus was God's son and they should follow him. Some of the people in Damascus didn't like this at all! They were so angry they made plans to kill Paul. But some of his friends heard about it and planned a daring escape for him.

Join the dots to discover how Paul escaped from the city and colour in the picture.

Barnabas was a follower of Jesus. He and Paul became friends and together they travelled around telling people about how Jesus wanted them to live. Barnabas' home was on an island. One day he said to Paul, "God has said to me that we should tell the people on my island about Jesus."

Write the first letter of the word for each picture in the centre of the picture wheel to find the name of Barnabas' island.

Barnabas and Paul went to the main town in Cyprus to tell people about Jesus. They visited the governor's palace. "Tell me about this Jesus," the governor said. But an evil magician did his best to stop the governor from believing in Jesus. Paul turned on him. "You enemy of God! He will punish you for this!" The man became blind, but the governor became a follower of Jesus.

Paul and Barnabas are talking to the governor. Find four things that are wrong in the picture.

Whenever Paul and Barnabas visited a town and talked about Jesus, some people believed and became followers of Jesus but others were angry. They did not want to hear about Jesus. In one city a mob followed the friends and picked up stones to throw at them. Paul and Barnabas had to get away quickly!

Help Paul and Barnabas escape through the maze from the angry crowd.

Paul and Barnabas arrived safely in Lystra and started telling people about Jesus. A lame man sat listening and Paul saw that he wanted to believe in Jesus. He said to the man, "Jesus can heal you. Stand up!" And the man, who had never walked before, stood up and jumped about.

Can you match the man with his shadow?

When the people of Lystra saw the lame man healed, they crowded around Paul and Barnabas. "They are gods from heaven," they said, and wanted to worship them. Paul and Barnabas were horrified. "No, we're just people, like you. God has healed this man, not us."

Unscramble the jumbled words to find out what Paul and Barnabas said to the people.

We are here to tell you about the only _____ God who made the
rute

_____ He gives you _____ and makes you _____
rowdl. ofod paphy.

Paul and Barnabas decided to part and go in different directions. Paul had two new helpers called Silas and Timothy. When Timothy was a little boy, his grandmother told him stories about Jesus. Timothy grew up wanting to tell other people about Jesus too.

Many years later Paul wrote a letter to Timothy. Use the code to find the missing words and see what Paul said.

H = △
L = ●
S = ⊠
U = ▼
I = ◆
Y = ✕
C = O
R = ■
E = +
P = ◈
T = ⋔
O = ⁒

Remember that ever since you were a child you have known the...

Paul always asked God to show him where he and his helpers should go next to tell people about Jesus. One night Paul had a very clear dream. In his dream he saw a man from Greece. "Come to Greece and help us!" the man begged him. So straightaway, Paul and his friends got ready to sail to Greece.

Join the dots to complete the ship.

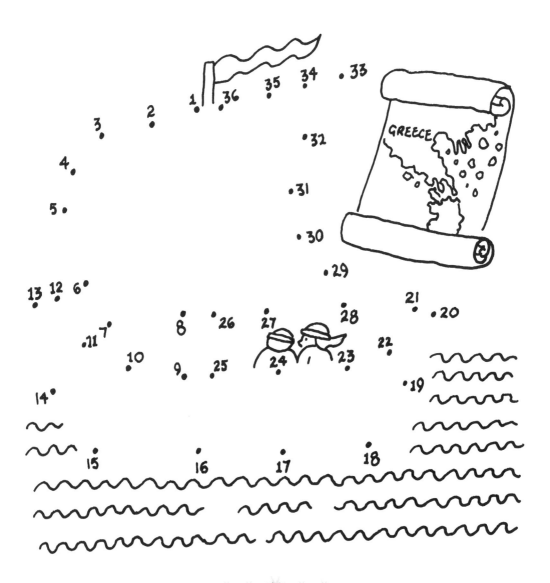

Paul and his helpers arrived in Greece and went to a town called Philippi. They wondered what God wanted them to do there. As they walked by the river, they met some women who wanted to hear about Jesus. One woman, who became a follower of Jesus, said to Paul and his friends, "Come and stay at my house."

Colour in the picture and use the code to find out the name of the kind woman.

One day Paul and his friends were walking along a street in Philippi. They were followed by a slave girl, who was a fortune-teller. She shouted, "These men are servants of God. They tell you how to be saved!" Paul knew that she had an evil spirit and he ordered the spirit, "In the name of Jesus, come out of her!" The girl was healed at once.

Find seven differences between the two pictures. (All the changes in the girl count as one difference!)

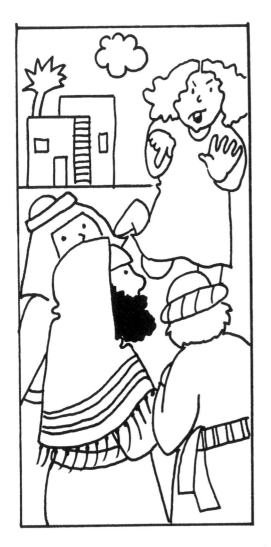

The fortune-teller girl used to earn a lot of money for her owners. When she became a believer in Jesus she stopped telling fortunes. Her owners were angry and attacked Paul and Silas. "These men are causing trouble in our city," they told the city officials.

Join the dots to find out what happened to Paul and Silas next and colour in the picture.

Paul was not surprised that he had to suffer
for telling people about Jesus.

It was midnight in the prison and the prisoners heard singing. It was Paul and Silas praising God! Suddenly there was a violent earthquake. The doors flew open and the chains fell off all the prisoners. The jailer woke up and thought the prisoners had escaped. He pulled out his sword to kill himself but a shout from Paul stopped him.

Put the words in the right order to discover what Paul said to the jailer.

_____ _____ _____!

_____ _____ _____ _____!

The jailer was shaking as he knelt at the feet of Paul and Silas. "What must I do to be saved?" he asked them. "Believe in the Lord Jesus," they told him. The jailer took them to his house and gave them some food. He and his family became followers of Jesus and were very happy.

Put the pictures of the story about Paul and Silas in the jail in the right order. Write the numbers 1 to 4 in the boxes.

A man called Aquila and his wife Priscilla lived in the city of Corinth. They made and sold tents and Paul lived with them for a while. Paul also earned some money by making tents but he told people about Jesus as well. Many people became believers in Jesus. One night God spoke to Paul in a dream. "Keep on speaking about me for I am with you," he said.

Find two tents with matching patterns and put a tick (✓) beside them.

When people believed in Jesus they stopped worshipping other gods. Followers of Jesus stopped buying silver models of the temple of the goddess Artemis and this upset the silversmiths who made the models. "This Paul is ruining our business. Get rid of him!" they urged the people. An angry mob shouted for two hours, "Great is Artemis of Ephesus!" God kept Paul safe but he had to leave the city.

Fill in the missing letters to see what God said to his people. Choose from e,i,o,u.

God said, "W_____rsh_____p   n_____

g_____d   b_____t   m_____."

Paul often held meetings in people's homes. One evening when he was talking to a crowd of people in an upstairs room, a young man sitting on the window ledge fell asleep. He fell out through the open window down to the ground. When his friends picked him up he was dead. Paul went downstairs, bent over the young man and hugged him.

Follow the letters as they fall and rise to discover what Paul said.

_____ _____ _____ _____

Paul travelled to Jerusalem and went into the temple to pray to God. Some Jews, who saw him there, told lies about him and stirred up trouble. They dragged Paul out of the temple and an angry crowd tried to kill him. But, just in time, he was rescued by Roman soldiers. "Take him to the fort!" their commander ordered.

Look carefully at this picture and find four things that should not be there.

The Roman commander allowed Paul to speak to the people from the steps of the fort. At first they listened to Paul, but soon they began screaming again, "Kill him!" The commander told a soldier to beat Paul to find out why the Jews were screaming against him. "Is it right to beat a Roman citizen who has done nothing wrong?" Paul asked. At this the commander turned pale with fear. Roman citizens had special protection and by hurting Paul he would be breaking the law!

Can you name all the parts of this Roman's uniform?

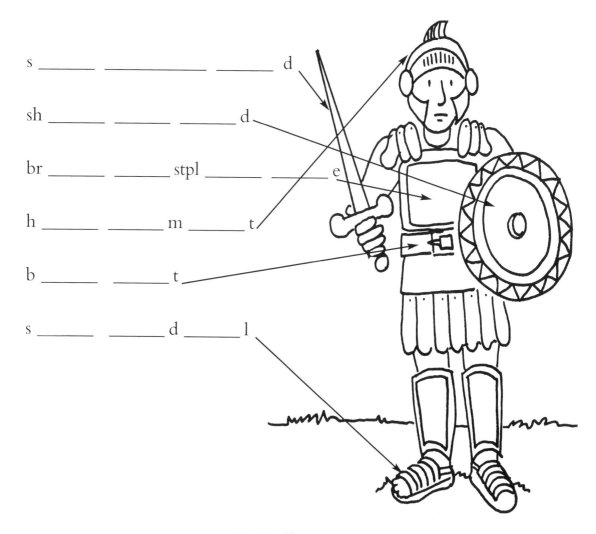

s _____ _____ _____ d

sh _____ _____ _____ d

br _____ _____ stpl _____ _____ e

h _____ _____ m _____ t

b _____ _____ t

s _____ _____ d _____ l

Paul was kept in the Roman fort while the commander tried to find out what he had done to annoy the Jews so much. Meanwhile the Jews plotted to kill him. But Paul's nephew found out about the plot and warned the commander secretly.

Use the code to work out the missing words in the secret message from Paul's nephew.

<u>tomorrow</u> you will be asked to
B3 D4 A1 D4 E1 E1 D4 C5

bring <u>Paul</u> to a <u>meeting</u>.
     A5 C2 E5 B5   A1 B1 B1 B3 D2 A3 E3

More than <u>forty</u> men will be
     C4 D4 E1 B3 A4

<u>hiding</u> and they will ambush and
B2 D2 D3 D2 A3 E3

<u>kill</u> Paul.
E4 D2 B5 B5

	1	2	3	4	5
A	m	b	n	y	p
B	e	h	t	c	l
C	j	a	q	f	w
D	s	i	d	o	v
E	r	x	g	k	u

The commander called his officers. "Get horses and an armed escort of soldiers ready for Paul and take him tonight to Caesarea. I'll give you a letter for the Roman governor there." So Paul rode away by night and escaped the plotters. He was taken to the Roman governor's palace and kept there under guard.

Can you work out how many men were in Paul's escort? Finish the words and add up the numbers.

200 s _ ld _ _ rs

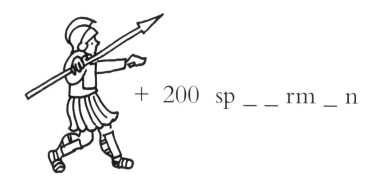

\+ 200 sp _ _ rm _ n

\+ _70_ h _ rs _ m _ n

=

Paul stayed in prison for a long time. At last he was sent to Rome to be tried by the emperor. One day Paul was put on a sailing ship for Italy. It was winter and the sailors hoped to reach a sheltered spot. But a strong wind blew up and before long the ship was in trouble.

Help the ship find the right channel through the rocks and past the islands.

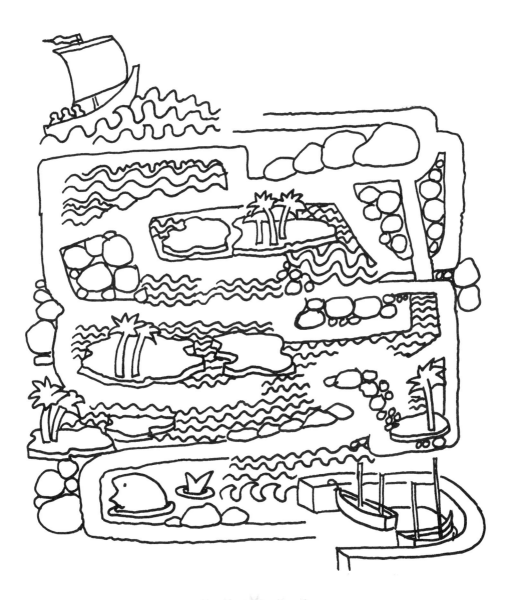

The storm went on for days and the sailors threw some of the cargo overboard to make the ship lighter. Nobody wanted to eat and everyone, except Paul, gave up hope of being saved. Paul told them, "Cheer up! God has told me that the ship will be lost but all our lives will be saved." Paul ate some bread and soon the others all ate too.

Circle all these words about the voyage in the wordsearch. Look across and down. Draw a ring around the words.

SAILORS, SHIP,
ANCHOR, CARGO, CAPTAIN,
WAVES, STORM, SEA, SAILS

Next morning the sailors saw land and decided to head for it. They tried to get the ship into a bay but it hit a sandbank and began to break up. Everyone jumped overboard and swam or floated on planks to the shore. They were all safe, as God had told Paul. They stayed on the island for the winter and then sailed away in another ship, bound for Rome.

Write the first letter of the word for each picture in the centre of the picture wheel to find out the name of the island where Paul landed.

ANSWERS

page 3	heart, soul, mind
page 5	Damascus
page 6	He could see and was baptised.
page 8	Cyprus
page 9	camera, watch, stereo, trainers
page 11	Shadow 3
page 12	true, world, food, happy
page 13	Holy Scriptures
page 15	Lydia
page 18	Don't harm yourself! We are all here!
page 21	Worship no god but me.
page 22	Don't worry, he is alive!
page 23	rabbit, suitcase, flowery hat, flowery skirt
page 24	sword, shield, breastplate, helmet, belt, sandal
page 25	Tomorrow, Paul, meeting, forty, hiding, kill
page 26	200 soldiers + 200 spearmen + 70 horsemen = 470
page 29	Malta

There are 3 more puzzle books in this series to collect.
Look out for them!

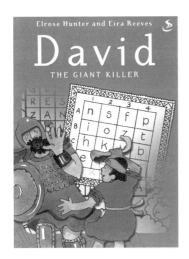

978 1 84427 076 7
£1.99

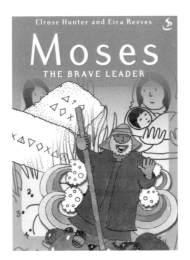

978 1 84427 075 0
£1.99

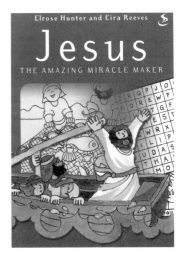

978 1 84427 077 4
£1.99

Look out for great puzzle books about Abraham, Joseph, Daniel and Peter!

You can buy all of these books at Christian bookshops,
online at www.scriptureunion.org.uk/publishing
or call Mail Order direct: 0845 0706 006

Have you had fun with this puzzle book? Then look out for the Join in – jump on! books. You will find stories about people in the Bible and lots of ideas to help you get to know God better. Each day you will find:

- something to read
- a puzzle or questions to answer
- something to look up in the Bible
- a prayer idea

Sometimes there are Extra fun ideas too!

There are six Join in – jump on! books.
Why not give them a try?

Stories from Luke... and more!

Stories from Mark... and more!

Stories for Easter... and more!

Stories from Matthew... and more!

Stories for Christmas... and more!

Stories from John... and more!

You can buy all of these books at Christian bookshops,
online at www.scriptureunion.org.uk/publishing
or call Mail Order direct: 08450 706 006